Poppy's Pot

Mal Peet

Illustrated by Ian Newsham

Oxford

Poppy got a pot.

Soil

Poppy put in some soil.

She put in some seeds.

Poppy put in some water.

What can we grow?

arrot   Potato   Lettuce

Sunflower

She put the pot in the sun.

Trees

Jane

roots

DUCK GREEN

FLOWER
SHOW

"Look!" said Poppy.

"Green hair!"